Wedding Vow Journal

YOUR GUIDE TO WRITING THE MOST ORIGINAL
TEAR-INDUCING, NON-BORING WEDDING VOWS
OF ALL TIME

For Z.

Table of Contents

Introduction

Picture your wedding day. You're standing at the altar hopeful, well dressed, and smelling fantastic. You're facing your partner, and the officiant asks you to read your vows. Someone in your bridal party hands you your *Wedding Vow Journal* where you've written them out. As you read, your heartfelt words move your guests to tears. Then you look into the teary, loving eyes of your partner and feel satisfied with your work.

Your vows were everything you hoped they would be and then some.

If you're holding this journal, you've probably imagined a similar scenario. Unless it was a gift, then you might be unnerved by the fact that you haven't imagined it at all. And if you're unnerved, you might be upset with whoever gave it to you. But before you pull out your phone and begin texting vulgarities to said gift-giver, listen up:

This journal is a guide full of writing exercises and engaging activities to help you navigate the challenging, emotional, and complex aspects of vow writing in a simple, lighthearted, and easy-to-follow format.

The single mission of this journal is to help you write the most original, tear-inducing, non-boring wedding vows of all time. It's not for goal setting, dream catching, or recording the reasons why you think your mother-in-law secretly hates you.

For the most beneficial writing experience, purchase the companion book for this journal, *Wedding Vow Writing: How to write the most original, tear-inducing, non-boring wedding vows of all time.*

Let's get started.

First up

Every couple is composed of two individuals, so agreeing on wedding vow details can be tricky. The willingness to compromise with your partner during this phase is important, especially if you're on opposite ends of the vow-writing spectrum. By learning how to compromise now, you're killing two proverbial birds with one proverbial stone: You're taking big steps in the writing process *and* preparing for the many compromises that you'll have to make in your upcoming marriage. Don't worry, though—no proverbial birds will be harmed in the process.

First up, let's ease the tension with some light-hearted wedding trivia and then make a few foundational decisions about the wedding vows that you and your partner are going to write.

Wedding Trivia

Answer the following trivia questions to the best of your ability. If your mental database of wedding facts fails you, you can find the answers on the following page.

1. What is the top wedding destination in the world?[1]

_____

2. Why does your wedding ring go on the 3rd finger of the left hand?[2]

_____

_____

3. What is the most popular wedding month in the United States?[1]

_____

4. Why does the groom traditionally stand with his right arm to his wedding guests?[2]

_____

_____

5. How much is spent on weddings every year in the U.S.?[1]

_____

1. Las Vegas. 2. The ancient Egyptians believed that the vein in the third finger of the left hand, which they called the "vein of love," ran directly to the heart. 3. June. 4. Historically, the groom's right hand, or his "sword hand," needed to be free to defend his bride against any man who wanted to steal her and make her his wife. 5. Approximately $72 billion.

Writing Exercises

(1.1) On a scale from 1 to 10, how do you feel about writing original wedding vows? (1 being "It's a terrible idea" and 10 being "Nothing would make me happier")

1   2   3   4   5   6   7   8   9   10

Ask your partner how he/she feels about writing original wedding vows on a scale from 1 to 10? (1 being "This is the worst idea you've ever had" and 10 being "I'm over the moon excited about this idea")

1   2   3   4   5   6   7   8   9   10

Where do you and your partner stand on the topic? If you're on opposite ends of the spectrum, you'll have to come to a compromise that you're both comfortable with. If you both chose a number between 8 and 10, skip ahead to exercise 1.3. If one or both of you chose numbers below 8, complete exercise 1.2.

(1.2) List the reasons why you chose the number you chose in exercise 1.1. If you chose a low number, list the reasons why you're hesitant to write original vows. If you chose a high number, list the reasons why it's important to you.

_____

_____

_____

_____

Ask your partner why he/she chose the number in section 1.1, and write the answer below. If it was a low number, list the reasons why he/she is hesitant to write original vows. If it was a high number, list the reasons why it's important to him/her.

_____

_____

_____

_____

Now that you know where you both stand, discuss a possible compromise. If your partner is uncomfortable with the idea, express the reasons why it's important to you, and brainstorm ways to make him/her feel more comfortable. Can you agree to write your vows together or to finish your vows far enough in advance so that you can easily make changes? Maybe you each agree to write one minute of original vows and close with a form of traditional wedding vows. If your partner is still uncomfortable with the idea even after this discussion, offer to write his/her vows instead.

If you're the one who's uncomfortable with the idea, do your best to meet your partner halfway. Maybe your partner has something important to say to you during the ceremony, or he/she is excited to express his/her love in a creative way. Whatever it is, use this opportunity to express your concerns and make a compromise, then write out the compromise below:

_____

_____

_____

_____

(1.3) It's time to discuss the details. Answer the following questions with your partner. Are you going to write your vows together or separately?

_____

How long will your vows be? Do your best to stay under ten minutes or between one and five minutes each.

_____

Do you want your vows to have similar structures?

_____

Will your vows have a theme? If so, what would it be?

_____

(1.4) Now that the first discussions are done and the foundational decisions have been made, it's time to set a due date. By doing this, you create a natural accountability with your partner to finish your vows. **Your due date should be at least two weeks before your wedding day** so that you have plenty of time to make adjustments and practice your delivery. This will also prevent you from procrastinating and adding more stress to an already stressful event. Select a due date for your vows, and write it below:

_____

Do your research

If you're a good student, then you know the importance of preparation. If you're a not-so-good student, then you're probably more familiar with the art of procrastination. In the case of vow writing, procrastination has nothing to offer you. It adds anxiety and tension to an already nerve-wracking situation; it causes you to be too rushed to write well-thought-out, meaningful words; and it fills you with regret when your vows weren't everything they could have been.

When it comes to your vows, it doesn't matter what kind of student you are. Choose preparation over procrastination... consider yourself warned.

In this section, you'll gather the information you need to lay a solid foundation for a compelling set of original, tear-inducing, non-boring wedding vows—which is a really wordy and intense way of saying that you'll do your research. You'll also reflect on the different aspects of your relationship, discuss your role models, learn a little bit about marriage, and practice writing some vows of your own.

Writing Exercises

(2.1) You and your partner will begin this section with a little relationship research. Plan a date to discuss the topics and answer the questions in this section. First, you'll take a walk down memory lane by discussing the following topics. Take notes on the next page.

How you met
Your first impressions of each other

Your first date
Your first kiss
When you knew your partner was the one

_____

_____

_____

_____

_____

_____

_____

_____

_____

_____

Next, you'll discuss the current state of your relationship. Think of it as a low-stakes DTR, because, well, you've already decided to commit your lives to each other. Answer the following questions with your partner:

How do you make each other better?

_____

_____

_____

_____

Do your research

What made this relationship stand out from the rest?

_____

_____

_____

_____

How do you handle conflict with each other?

_____

_____

_____

What are your favorite things about your relationship?

_____

_____

_____

Why did you choose to get married?

_____

_____

_____

The last thing you'll talk about is your future. Your wedding day is the first day of the rest of your life...for better or for worse. Discuss the following topics, and take notes in the space below.

What can you do to cultivate a healthy marriage relationship?
How do you plan to grow as individuals and as a couple?
What values do you share, and how will they affect your future?
How do you hope to handle success and failure?
Where do you see yourselves 5, 10, even 40 years from now?

_____

_____

_____

_____

_____

_____

_____

_____

(2.2) It takes time to learn how to be married, which is why having role models from the start can be helpful. In this section, you'll select a couple to be your marriage role models, and you'll analyze the reasons why you admire them. If you don't know any couples with happy, healthy marriages, do some research, and find a couple to look up to, like your great-grandparents or Jay-Z and Beyoncé.

Who are your marriage role models? _____

What do you admire about this couple's marriage?

How can you emulate the things you admire about their marriage in your own relationship?

(2.3) Just because you chose to write your own vows doesn't mean you have to be 100% original. With a little research, you can ease your workload by imitating your favorite writer, rewording a love song, or using a wedding vow guide...like this one.

Fill in the following guide to practice vow writing. If you love what you come up with, use it in your vows.

When I met you, _____

_____

_____

(List the ways your life changed after you met your partner.)

I never want to live without _____

17

_____

_____

_____

_____.

(Write down the traits that you couldn't live without.)

Every day, you inspire me to _____

_____

_____

_____

_____.

(Talk about the ways your partner inspires you every day.)

I promise to _____

_____

_____

_____

_____.

(Write the promises you want to make to your partner.)

Marriage Research

ON AVERAGE
married couples
HAVE SEX 58 TIMES A YEAR.

the LONGEST MARRIAGE
EVER *recorded lasted* 91 YEARS:

marriage helps people
BE HAPPIER: LIVE LONGER
SLEEP BETTER:
RECOVER from ILLNESS QUICKER
and HAVE BETTER PHYSICAL & MENTAL HEALTH

Final preparations

The engagement season fills up your plate in a uniquely overwhelming way. It doesn't matter how many tasks make it on your list; there's always more to do. But before you throw your full plate out the window and cry "No more," remind yourself that this is only a season, and it's a season during which *you're the boss.* Full plates are more bearable when you get to be the boss, right?

There are only a few final preparations before you start writing. Once they're done, you can remove one more task from your plate...and then replace it with another one that you forgot about. This section will guide you as you get advice, get creative, and get inspired.

Writing Exercises

(3.1) So why do you need advice? Because marriage is unlike any other experience or relationship you've ever had. If you want your vows to reflect the realities of marriage, you'll need to talk to someone who's actually been there. Unless, of course, you'd prefer to wing it.

Make a list of the people in your life who you admire that have happy, healthy marriages:

_____

_____

_____

_____

_____

Would any of these people be available to meet with you before you begin writing your vows? If so, set an appointment to get advice. Here is a list of suggested questions for you to ask when you meet:

What surprised you the most about being married?

_____

_____

_____

_____

What do you wish you knew before you got married?

_____

_____

_____

_____

What roadblocks or struggles should we expect?

_____

_____

_____

_____

What important things should we remember as newlyweds?

_____

_____

_____

_____

What is your best marriage advice?

_____

_____

_____

(3.2) It's time to get creative by adding a little flair to your wedding vows, and there are countless ways to do it. Keep in mind that whatever you do should mirror your personality.

> If you're a writer, quote your favorite author.
> If you have a different native language, say something in it.
> If you're funny, add a few jokes.
> If you're a musician, write a song.

You get the picture. Examine the talents and personality traits that make you unique, and brainstorm creative ways to express them.

On the other hand, you might not have a creative bone in your body...and that's okay too. A wildly creative element would be more out of character than romantic. If that's the case, move on to the next section and never look back.

(3.3) It's possible that you've felt a little uninspired by the process so far, but just like any worthwhile endeavor, writing your own vows takes time and dedication. So, when you feel yourself dragging or unmotivated, seek out a little inspiration to get yourself going again. Not sure where to turn? Check out the popular, romantic inspirations below:

Movies: *When Harry Met Sally*
The Notebook
You've Got Mail
Pretty Woman
Sleepless in Seattle

Songs: "I Will Always Love You" by Whitney Houston
"When a Man Loves a Woman" by Percy Sledge
"Endless Love" by Diana Ross and Lionel Richie
"I Want to Know What Love Is" by Foreigner
"I'm Yours" by Jason Mraz

Novels: *Jane Eyre* by Charlotte Brontë
A Walk to Remember by Nicholas Sparks
Redeeming Love by Francine Rivers
Outlander by Diana Gabaldon
The Duke and I by Julia Quinn

Now, list your favorite romantic inspirations below.

Romantic movie: _____

Love song: _____

Romance novel: _____

The next time you need a boost to work on your wedding vows, watch, listen to, or read one of the inspirations above. Romantic comedies have never been so useful.

Wedding Crossword

Across

1. The bundle of flowers that the bride throws at her single friends during the reception.
2. Guidance from experienced, married role models—*hint in exercise 3.1.*
3. The often stressful, sometimes chaotic, but always worth it event that you host to celebrate your marriage.
4. What you're being when you artistically personalize your vows—*hint in exercise 3.2.*
5. Men supporting the groom who can usually be found heavy drinking at the reception (or all day long).
6. Rhythmic, lovely movement to music that is too often neither rhythmic nor lovely.
7. What you need to be to get motivated to work on your vows—*hint in exercise 3.3.*
8. The pathway that the bride walks on as she walks toward her groom and the altar.
9. Speeches given at the reception with a beverage in hand.

Down

1. The post-wedding dance party where guests are given too many opportunities to make regrettable decisions.
2. A woman who supports the bride by crying, laughing, shouting, and dancing at the wedding...sometimes all at once.
3. The reason you're having a wedding in the first place.
4. Promises you make to your partner at the altar, and the entire reason you're using this journal in the first place.
5. The person responsible for marrying the couple and announcing them as husband and wife.
6. People who attend a wedding to witness a marriage and to receive free food and cake.

Crossword Answer Key

Choose a structure

There are plenty of pros and cons to writing your own wedding vows, but one of the biggest pros is flexibility. You have so many options to choose from when it comes to structure, tone, and even verbiage. Unfortunately, this abundance can also create more work for you, resulting in decision paralysis (the lesser known, less fun to say cousin of analysis paralysis).

The trick is knowing your options, choosing the one that fits you the best, and seeking guidance when you need it. Just because you're writing original vows doesn't mean you have to be totally original. After all, everything's been done before, so borrowing ideas and learning from professionals isn't wrong; it's wise. Get ready—the exercises in this section are designed to ease decision paralysis and help you choose a structure that's right for you.

Writing Exercises

(4.1) You didn't know there were multiple options for structuring your wedding vows, did you? Explore your options below.

Combine traditional and original vows.

What is it? A structure that combines original vows with any version of traditional vows.

Pros: You get the best of both worlds: originality and tradition.
Cons: Even though you save time and energy by using traditional vows, all of those "saved" resources are used to write original vows.

Example: "You are my priority and my greatest ally. I promise to treasure you from this day forward, for better or for worse, for richer or for poorer, in sickness and in health, until death do us part."

Read the same original vows.

What is it? The couple recites the same, pre-written original wedding vows to one another.

Pros: Since only one set of vows has to be written, it's less work for the couple. **Cons:** The vows will be less personalized since they have to apply to both parties.

Example: The bride and the groom both read the following vow to each other: "You are the reason I want to be the best version of myself, and I will spend the rest of my days loving you the way you need to be loved."

Write complementary vows.

What is it? A structure where both sets of vows are written to complement each other, either with similar themes, the same closing statement, or another complementary element.

Pros: They give the ceremony a well-planned, cohesive feel. **Cons:** It's difficult to agree and collaborate on a creative, complementary element.

Example: The bride and groom are both avid hikers, so they decide to write vows with a lot of nature imagery like, "I promise to encourage you through the valleys and celebrate with you on the mountaintops."

Deliver call-and-response vows.

What is it? A back-and-forth style where one partner reads a line that's quickly followed by a related response from the other partner, and this continues for the duration of the vows.

Pros: They flow well and indicate unity. **Cons:** This structure is a collaborative effort that requires a lot of time and planning.

Example: One partner says, "You taught me how to love without boundaries," and the other responds, "You tore down all of the walls I built up around my heart."

(4.2) There are plenty of ways to highlight who you are in your vows. Answer the following questions to begin gathering personalized elements, and let your personality shine through.

What three personality traits best describe you? Brainstorm ways that you can incorporate them into your vows.

1. _____

_____

_____

2. _____

_____

_____

3. _____

_____

_____

List three things that you feel passionate about and how you can incorporate them into your vows.

1. _____

_____

_____

2. _____

_____

_____

3. _____

_____

_____

Is there a love quote that beautifully summarizes or describes your relationship? Write it below, then include it in your vows as is or personalize it by rewriting it.

_____

_____

_____

_____

(4.3) Review examples of the four vow structures below, and then decide which one you'll use with your partner. If you love a line or two from the examples, feel free to borrow or remix them as you wish. Don't obsess over being original.

Example: Combine traditional and original vows.

You are my perfect match. I never knew what I needed in a life partner, but that changed after you taught me what it meant to love someone. You blow me away every day with how well you love me. I'm forever grateful for the encourager, adventurer, and lover you so naturally are. In the name of God, I, [name], take you, [partner's name], to be my wife/husband, to have and to hold from this day forward, for better, for worse, for richer, for poorer, in sickness and in health, to love and to cherish, until we are parted by death. This is my solemn vow.

Example: The same original vows.

[Partner's name], I want you exactly as you are. Loving you has been the greatest honor of my life. From this day forward, I promise to choose compromise over pride. I promise to celebrate your wins and hold you close through your losses. I will be your biggest supporter and advocate. You are my best friend. Today, I take you, [partner's name], as my lawfully wedded husband/wife.

Example: Complementary vows.

Husband: I, [name], take you, [partner's name], to be my wife. I love all of the things I know about you, and I trust that I'll love what I discover in the future. When things get hard, I promise to swallow my pride, carry my part of the burden, and walk beside you every day. I promise to support your dreams and share your goals. Our future is so bright. I can't wait to start a family with you. You are my motivation, my first priority, and the love of my life. I am yours from this day forward.

Wife: I, [name], take you, [partner's name], to be my husband. Every part of me is in love with every part of you, even the parts I don't know yet. When the world isn't kind to us, and we're overcome by struggles, I promise to support you the best way I know how. I promise to share in all of your dreams and to encourage you when you feel like giving up. I look forward to the beautiful life we're going to build together. You are going to be the best dad. You are my strength, my inspiration, and the love of my life. I am devoted to you from this day forward.

Example: Call-and-response vows.

Husband: [Partner's name], I've known since we met that I wanted to make you my wife. Your smile overwhelmed me, and you spoke with such grace and kindness. You are unlike any person I've ever known.

Wife: [Partner's name], I knew I wanted to be with you forever after our third date. Watching you handle your struggles with integrity and a willingness to learn inspired me to look inward. You make me want to be a better person.

Husband: You teach me something new and beautiful every day. The lens through which you see your life is so full of joy. It's contagious.

Wife: You have a way of making me feel seen and loved like I've never experienced. Your life is a reflection of your courage, determination, and authenticity.

Husband: I promise to stand by your side when we experience the many trials of life. And when there are trials in our marriage, I promise to be humble and to always be willing to learn and grow.

Wife: I promise I won't run away when things get hard; instead, I'll support and honor you. I also promise to own my mistakes, even when I'm feeling stubborn, and to handle yours with grace.

Husband: You are mine, to have and to hold, for better or for worse, for richer or for poorer. Anywhere that life takes us, I promise that I'm not going anywhere.

Wife: You are mine, in sickness and in health, to love and to cherish, until we are parted by death. I promise to love you the selflessly every day.

Husband: Today, I take you, [partner's name], as my wife.

Wife: Today, I take you, [partner's name], as my husband.

Wedding Traditions

Have you ever wondered why brides throw bundles of foliage at their friends or wear a long piece of fabric on their heads at their weddings? If you're unaware of their historical and cultural contexts, some of these traditions might seem strange or pointless. Find the origins of some of the most common wedding traditions below.

Wearing a wedding veil. The veil traditionally symbolized youth and virginity, and it "hid" the bride from evil spirits… which were apparently a major concern in ancient wedding ceremonies. In the Victorian era, the white veil became popular as a symbol of modesty and purity.[2]

Carrying a bouquet. Roman brides kept herbs under their veils to symbolize fidelity and fertility and to protect themselves from evil spirits. The tradition evolved into the modern bridal bouquet, which exists less to ward off evil and more to look fabulous.[2]

Not allowing the groom to see the bride before the wedding ceremony. This tradition began when arranged marriages were popular and grooms might never have seen their brides. If that was the case, preventing him from seeing her before the ceremony might reduce the chances of him running away if she didn't visually please him.[3] How terrible is that for both parties involved? "I wouldn't have married you if they hadn't tricked me…"

Consuming wedding cake. Cake has been a part of wedding celebrations since Roman times because it traditionally symbolizes fertility and good luck…and because everything is better with cake. The Romans would break a small bun above the bride's head, and in the Middle Ages, the bride and groom had to kiss over cakes.[2]

Tossing the bouquet and garter. In ancient times, wedding guests would tear off pieces of the bride's wedding gown (umm…rude?) for good luck. This practice eventually led to her handing out her bouquet and garter as good luck tokens.[2]

Set your tone

The tone you set for your vows will be the difference between tears, laughter, and guests squirming uncomfortably in their seats. If you want tears, write vows that are poetic and heartfelt. If you want laughter, add humor. If you want uncomfortable squirming, overshare about your sex life or refer to the "D" word…which is *Divorce* in this context. (*Damn* is exponentially more acceptable in a wedding ceremony than *Divorce*.)

In this section, you'll set the tone for your vows. You can make them feel light, serious, fun, or genuine—whatever you prefer. It's your big day, so the decision is yours. And just in case you were unsure, your goal should *not* be to make your guests squirm uncomfortably.

Writing Exercises

(5.1) So what does it look like to pick a tone? It's not as tricky as it sounds. See the examples below.

"I grew up in a religious home, so I want my vows to have a religious theme but also feel compelling and authentic."

"I'm going to write honest vows that are full of heartfelt lines, but I want them to be packed with imagery and have a whimsical feel to reflect my creative personality."

"Since my fiancé and I love to laugh together, I want to write humorous vows that still have an intimate feel."

"I want my vows to be romantic, but I also want them to reflect the more analytical and reserved side of my personality."

(5.2) Before you pick a tone, you'll want a personality vocabulary. Start by circling the three words below that best describe you:

Practical	**Lighthearted**	**Serious**	**Honest**
Ambitious	**Considerate**	**Funny**	**Courageous**
Passionate	**Generous**	**Reliable**	**Thoughtful**
Religious	**Adventurous**	**Romantic**	**Philosophical**

Next, circle the three words that best describe your partner:

Practical	**Lighthearted**	**Serious**	**Honest**
Ambitious	**Considerate**	**Funny**	**Courageous**
Passionate	**Generous**	**Reliable**	**Thoughtful**
Religious	**Adventurous**	**Romantic**	**Philosophical**

If there are any words that better describe you and your partner that weren't mentioned above, list them below.

You: _____

_____

_____

_____

Your Partner: _____

_____

_____

_____

Now that you have a personality vocabulary, it's time for you and your partner to articulate the tone that you want to use. Keep this description as concise as possible so that it's easy to remember as you write your vows. If you need guidance, reference the examples in section 5.1.

_____

_____

_____

_____

_____

_____

(5.3) As you set the tone for your vows, it's important to make sure that you're not overdoing it with clichés. Complete the following clichés and do your best not to overuse them when you write your vows. You can find the answers below.

You make my _____ skip a _____.

Love is _____.

All is fair in _____ and _____.

_____ over _____ in love.

_____ and make up.

> 1. You make my heart skip a beat. 2. Love is blind. 3. All is fair in love and war. 4. Head over heels in love. 5. Kiss and make up.

Wedding Word Search

```
V L I A T K C O C E V O
C O F I A J O U R N A L
A Y L S B R I S U S T I
K A O L I E D G S E H N
C D W E D D I N G V O W
I G E I A I W I G R N O
T I R L Y A E R T E E L
N B S O J M O U R N Y F
A I L V N O E K A C M S
M N O O M N O H K I O C
O S W O V D T A N L O V
R O O M A E C G U S N E
```

AISLE	DIAMOND	LOVE
BIG DAY	FLOWERS	NERVES
BRIDE	GROOM	RINGS
CAKE	HONEYMOON	ROMANTIC
COCKTAIL	JOURNAL	WEDDING VOW

Put pen to paper

You knew this day would come. Preparations are complete, and decisions have been made. Now it's time to put your pen to paper and keep yourself from crumbling under the pressure.

The exercises in this section will guide you as you begin writing your actual vows. If it takes some of the pressure off for you to still think of them as practice vows, you're welcome to pretend. Keep in mind that, before you finish this journal, you will have to write your final wedding vows—that's kind of the point.

Writing Exercises

(6.1) This first exercise will help you turn qualities that you love about your partner into vows. You'll start by listing a quality, giving an example, and then forming it into a vow. See the example below, and then, complete the exercise for three of your partner's qualities.

Quality: He's kindhearted.

Example: He treats everyone he encounters with kindness and respect. He holds the door open for strangers, asks cashiers about their day, and treats people with patience and understanding...even when he gets cut off in rush hour traffic.

Vow: You are compassionate and so full of love. Everyone who comes in contact with you is better for it. You are the most kindhearted person I've ever met, and I promise to reciprocate and learn from that kindness as best I can.

Quality: _____

Example: _____

_____

_____

_____

Vow: _____

_____

_____

_____

_____

Quality: _____

Example: _____

_____

_____

_____

Vow: _____

_____

_____

_____

_____

Quality: _____

Example: _____

_____

_____

_____

Vow: _____

_____

_____

_____

(6.2) Now that you're on a roll, it's time to dive a little deeper. Answer the following questions, and explore the things that are just below the surface of your relationship. If an answer resonates with you, be sure to include it in your vows.

What has your partner taught you about yourself?

_____

_____

_____

_____

How do you and your partner make each other better people?

_____

_____

_____

How do you and your partner show love to each other every day?

_____

_____

_____

_____

How can you be intentional about cultivating a healthy marriage?

_____

_____

_____

_____

(6.3) Speaking of that roll you're on, it's time to create an outline. Review the outline example below, and then use the following blank pages to begin on your own. As you work through your journal, adjust your outline accordingly.

Outline Example

- Why I Picked You
  - You're beautifully selfless
  - You're strong willed & fight for what you want
  - I think it's cute when you're stubborn
  - I've never met another person who I connect with like I do with you
- Insert Story About My Grandparents Inspiring Love Story
- Why I Think This Is Going To Work
  - We both value our faith & families
  - We're both open to learning and growing through challenges in our relationship
  - We share the belief that selflessness is a critical foundation for marriage
  - We're willing to put in the work that it takes
- The Promises I Want To Make
  - I promise to love you more than anyone in the world
  - I promise to never go to bed angry
  - I promise to try to be understanding even when I think you're being a crazy person
  - I promise to seek wholeness as an individual so that I'm not relying on you to complete me
- Include Lines From Traditional Methodist Wedding Vows

Vow Outline

_____

_____

_____

_____

_____

_____

_____

_____

_____

_____

_____

_____

_____

_____

_____

_____

_____

_____

_____

_____

Put pen to paper

Vow-Libs

_____, I've known since
PARTNER'S NAME

_____ that you are
WHEN YOU KNEW YOUR PARTNER WAS THE ONE

the one I want to spend my life
with. I'm in love with every part of
you, your _____ and
PERSONALITY TRAIT YOU LOVE

your _____, even your
PERSONALITY TRAIT YOU LOVE

_____. You've taught
QUIRKY TRAIT OR HABIT

me how to _____ and
LESSON YOU'VE LEARNED FROM YOUR PARTNER

you love me _____. I want
ADVERB

to spend the rest of my life

_____ and _____
VERB + ING   VERB + ING

with you. Thank you for being my

_____. I love you.
NOUN

Dig in

It doesn't matter if your love story packs a romantic punch; articulating that romance can be a challenge. Especially if the last thing you wrote was for your ninth-grade English class, and your paper was about the symbolic relationship between Scout and Atticus in *Animal Farm*.[4]

Fortunately, there's an easier way: You dig into the details. When you think of your relationship in a timeline format, you cover all of your bases. By the end of this section, you'll have dug deep enough into your romance to generate solid material for your vows.

Nearly Newlyweds Game

Test your knowledge about your partner by answering the following questions. Then, compare your answers to your partner's answers.

Question	Your Answer	Partner's Answer
What is your partner's favorite color?		
What is your partner's favorite thing about you?		
How many children does your partner want?		

What is your partner's
favorite city?

_____   _____

Who is your partner's
best friend?

_____   _____

What is your partner's
favorite dessert?

_____   _____

Where is your
partner's ideal date?

_____   _____

Who is a better cook,
you or your partner?

_____   _____

Writing Exercises

(7.1) Take a walk down memory lane by creating a list of your
favorite memories with your partner. Think about when you met,
your first kiss, your first date, etc. Write your three favorites below.

1. _____

_____

_____

_____

2. _____

_____

_____

_____

3. _____

_____

_____

_____

(7.2) Now that you've dwelled on the past, it's time to come back to the present by answering questions about how your relationship functions today. What does your relationship look like on a daily basis? Why do you and your partner work well together? How do you respect each other as individ Now that you've dwelled on the pas uals while, at the same time, growing closer together? How do you support each other emotionally? Write a brief summary below about the current state of your relationship.

_____

_____

_____

_____

_____

_____

_____

_____

_____

(7.3) While your wedding day is definitely about celebrating your love story and present relationship, it's also about the vows (or promises) that you're making to each other for the future. List three promises below that you want to make to your partner on your wedding day.

Promise #1 _____

_____

_____

_____

Promise #2 _____

_____

_____

_____

Promise #3 _____

_____

_____

_____

(7.4) Take a deep breath—the following blank pages are for your first rough draft. You've collected plenty of great content, so now, your job is to pick your favorite parts, use the structure and the tone that you chose, and get to work. This draft should be exactly that…rough. Don't focus on perfection; instead, double-space your work so that you can adjust, correct, and organize as you go. You've got this.

Dig in

Dig in

Dig in

Dig in

_____

_____

_____

_____

_____

_____

_____

_____

_____

_____

_____

_____

_____

_____

_____

_____

_____

_____

_____

_____

Dig in

Find your voice

You've been told to "be yourself" from the moment you emerged from the womb. But with very little experience at this whole being-human thing, you learned early on to imitate the words and actions of your parents. Then, at some point, you learned from your peers that acting like your parents, being unique, and standing out were less than ideal. So it's no wonder that, even as an experienced adult, you might find it hard to be yourself and find your voice.

All original, tear-inducing, non-boring wedding vows have one thing in common: curse words—just kidding. They're authentic. Your vows can't be authentic if you're imitating someone else's words or voice. They have to be true to you. If you're not totally sure how to do that, the following exercises will guide you through a process of reflection, refinement, and rehearsal to help you find your voice.

Love Quote Quiz

This challenge is designed to give you a better understanding of voice so that you can begin articulating your own. Read through the following famous love quotes, and circle the name of the person who said it. Pay attention to the voice in each quote to figure out the answer. Answers are on the following page.

1. "You know you're in love when you can't fall asleep because reality is finally better than your dreams."[5]

Chuck Jones   Dr. Seuss   Jim Carrey

2. "Love is something sent from Heaven to worry the Hell out of you."[6]

Taylor Swift   Paul McCartney   Dolly Parton

3. "Love is composed of a single soul inhabiting two bodies."[7]

Aristotle   Jimi Hendrix   Gandhi

4. "There is no remedy for love but to love more."[8]

Oscar Wilde   Walt Whitman   Henry David Thoreau

5. "Darkness cannot drive out darkness; only light can do that. Hate cannot drive out hate; only love can do that."[9]

John F. Kennedy   Bob Dylan   Martin Luther King, Jr.

6. "Love is a smoke and is made with the fume of sighs."[10]

Charles Dickens   Jane Austen   William Shakespeare

7. "Love is a promise; love is a souvenir, once given never forgotten, never let it disappear."[11]

John Lennon   Elton John   Mick Jagger

1. Dr. Seuss 2. Dolly Parton 3. Aristotle 4. Henry David Thoreau 5. Martin Luther King, Jr. 6. William Shakespeare 7. John Lennon

Writing Exercises

(8.1) Let's start by defining your voice. Are you typically funny, lighthearted, and fun loving? Or are you more analytical, serious, and sarcastic? See the example, and define your voice below.

Example: *I'm artistic and outspoken, so I tend to speak directly to people and tell a lot of stories.*

_____

_____

_____

(8.2) Now that you've defined your voice, it's time to practice using it. Rewrite the following basic vow lines to make them sound like something you would say.

You are the most important person in my life.

_____

_____

My days are better because of you.

_____

_____

I love you so much.

_____

_____

I promise to encourage and support you.

_____

_____

I've never been happier.

_____

_____

(8.3) Define, practice…and revise. Go back to your rough draft, and read through it. Adjust words, phrasing, and sentences to sound like your voice. One of the best ways to determine if something sounds true to you is to read it out loud and see if it sounds like something you would actually say. Then, read through your revised rough draft multiple times to ensure that it sounds like your voice.

Make adjustments

From researching to writing, you've put in some serious work thus far. You felt the pressure of the process but pushed through anyway—not because you're some pressure-resistant brain surgeon or undercover agent, but because you're dedicated. Sure, you weren't poking your way around someone's brain or going undercover with your life on the line, but you vulnerably articulated feelings that will be shared in front of a group of people on your big day…and that can feel like the same thing.

Now that you've done the work, it's time to make adjustments. You'll start by reviewing what you wrote with consideration for your wedding guests. Next, you'll remove excess content and get feedback from someone close to you. And, by the end of this section, you'll be ready to make some finishing touches.

Writing Exercises

(9.1) Even though your vows are for you and your partner, it's wise to consider your audience in the process. For example, some things aren't appropriate to talk about in front of your wedding guests. And while this might sound like overkill, you'd be surprised how many people aren't as aware as they should be.

In this exercise, you'll read examples of questionable vows and then determine whether they're appropriate or inappropriate for your wedding guests by writing *Appropriate* or *Inappropriate* in the blank to the right of the line. You can find the answers below.

1. "Before I met you, I was selfish,   _____
   bitter and lonely."

2. "In my life, I've never experienced
   sexual freedom like I have with you."   _____

3. "My father (who is sitting on the
   front row) never showed me that he
   loved me, so our loving relationship
   has changed my life."   _____

4. "You always tell me how weak and
   insecure you are, and I want to spend
   the rest of my life showing you that
   you're worthy of love."   _____

5. "I promise to be sexually selfless
   at least 50% of the time, to take
   my antipsychotics regularly, and
   to pretend to enjoy your mother's
   visits."   _____

If you finish this exercise and realize that you might've
mentioned something inappropriate (or questionable) in your
vows, consider rewriting it for the sake of your guests…and
never speak of it again.

> 1. Appropriate 2. Inappropriate 3. Inappropriate
> 4. Appropriate 5. Inappropriate

(9.2) After you adjust your vows and make them wedding-guest-
friendly, you'll need to time them, make a few more adjustments,
and write a second draft. First, set a timer, and read your vows
out loud. You've likely collected way more content than you
need in this journal, so keep in mind that your vows should be

between one and five minutes long. If they're too long, begin crossing out the parts that you can exclude in your second draft. If they're too short, read back through your journal to see what you can add. Then, use the following blank pages to write a second draft.

_____

_____

_____

_____

_____

_____

_____

_____

_____

_____

_____

_____

_____

_____

_____

_____

Make adjustments

Make adjustments

_____

_____

_____

_____

_____

_____

_____

_____

_____

_____

_____

_____

_____

_____

_____

_____

_____

_____

_____

_____

_____

_____

_____

_____

_____

Make adjustments

Make adjustments

_____

_____

_____

_____

_____

_____

_____

_____

_____

_____

_____

_____

_____

_____

_____

_____

_____

_____

_____

_____

_____

(9.3) Now that you have your second draft complete, it's time to get feedback from a trusted source. Read your vows out loud to someone who knows you well. Ask questions like, "Are my vows a good length? Did they sound like my voice? Did the structure and tone fit my personality?" Record the feedback below.

_____

_____

_____

_____

_____

_____

_____

_____

Wedding Word Scramble

In the spirit of making adjustments, give your mind a break by adjusting the scrambled, wedding-related words below. You can find the answers on the following page.

GGAETNEENM   _____

EASHRALRE NRDIEN   _____

OUBUTEQ   _____

EDGWDIN IGSNR   _____

Wedding Vow Journal

NOMCERYE   _____

FIRST SKIS   _____

UBSHADN DAN EIWF _____

STICONTARNOAGUL   _____

AMREGRIA   _____

YOONONEHM   _____

1. Engagement 2. Rehearsal Dinner 3. Bouquet 4. Wedding Rings 5. Ceremony 6. First Kiss 7. Husband and Wife 8. Congratulations 9. Marriage 10. Honeymoon

94

Finishing touches

Welcome to the final section of your *Wedding Vow Journal*. It's been a marathon full of hills, water breaks, and stomach cramps, but you're almost to the finish line. Sadly, there won't be a free t-shirt or an unripe banana waiting for you at the end, but there will be blank, lined pages that are ready for the final version of your vows. And even though you should be proud of yourself, do your best not to obnoxiously reference this accomplishment in every conversation like marathoners do…that will *not* earn you any high-priced wedding gifts.

In this section, you'll learn some delivery basics, practice your vows, and write your final draft. Then you'll give your brain a break with a heart-shaped wedding vow maze because…why the hell not.

Writing Exercises

(10.1) Delivering your wedding vows can be one of the most intimidating parts of the process, but you've come too far to turn back now. If you want a confident and authentic delivery, here are a few things for you to keep in mind.

First, you're going to be nervous. You know how your body responds to nerves, so you should be prepared for it. Practice your vows out loud to minimize shaky vocals, chug Pepto-Bismol for your anxious stomach, and take a deep breath or two before you begin. Whatever you need to do, do it. You'll be thankful you were proactive about your nerves.

Next, make eye contact…with the right person. Your officiant, wedding party, and even a few wedding guests might be in your line of vision while you're delivering your vows, but try not to get distracted by them. Your eyes should move back and forth between your vows and your partner.

Finally, don't be afraid to get emotional. Crying is a vulnerable thing, and the words you wrote in your wedding vows are vulnerable too. As a matter of fact, if vulnerability isn't really your thing, you may want to reconsider having any wedding guests at all. But your better option is to get comfortable with the idea now. Your wedding day is a big deal, and it's normal to feel the weight of your emotions during your ceremony, especially while you're exchanging vows.

(10.2) You know what they say: practice makes perfect. That's why you should practice reading through your final vows at least ten times before your wedding day. Use the check boxes below.

☐ 1st Practice Date: _____

☐ 2nd Practice Date: _____

☐ 3rd Practice Date: _____

☐ 4th Practice Date: _____

☐ 5th Practice Date: _____

☐ 6th Practice Date: _____

☐ 7th Practice Date: _____

☐ 8th Practice Date: _____

☐ 9th Practice Date: _____

☐ 10th Practice Date: _____

(10.3) Can you believe it? It's time to write the final draft of your vows. Use the following blank pages to write a clean copy of your vows for your wedding day. If you'd prefer to read from a blank notebook or another place during the ceremony, use these pages to write a final draft, and then transfer it over.

Wedding Vow Maze

GET TO
THE HEART
OF YOUR VOWS

My Wedding Vows

_____

_____

_____

_____

_____

_____

_____

_____

_____

_____

_____

_____

_____

_____

_____

_____

_____

_____

_____

Conclusion

You did it. You finished your vows, and you're one step closer to exchanging heartfelt promises at the altar. That hopeful picture you had in your mind of your wedding day is about to be realized. Now all you have to worry about is dressing well and smelling fantastic…and maybe a few other details.

Hopefully the exercises and activities in this journal helped you better navigate the challenging, emotional, and complex aspects of vow writing. If your vows are original, tear-inducing, and non-boring, then your hipster cousin will be impressed, the bridesmaids will cry, and every grandfather in the room will remain awake for the duration of the ceremony…which is nothing short of a vow-writing success. Congratulations.

The only thing left for you to do is to marry the person of your dreams. Go get 'em.

Appendix

---

[1] Post, P. (2006). Emily Post's wedding etiquette. New York, NY: HarperCollins.

[2] Mullins, K. C. (1984). Bride's book of etiquette. New York, NY: Perigee Books.

[3] Lee, V. (1994). Something old, something new: What you didn't know about wedding ceremonies, celebrations & customs. Naperville, IL: Sourcebooks.

[4] Orwell, G. (1954). Animal farm. New York, NY: Harcourt, Brace, and World.

[5] Brockway, R. L. (n.d.). 14 Famous Quotes About Soulmates to Use in Your Wedding. Retrieved September 29, 2016, from

http://www.huffingtonpost.com/rev-laurie-sue-brockway/14-famous-quotes-about-soulmate_b_5268769.html

[6] Parton, D. (2010, July 26). "Love is something sent from HEAVEN to worry the HELL out of you!" :) - Dolly. Retrieved September 29, 2016, from https://twitter.com/dollyparton/status/19583457494

[7] Aristotle. (n.d.). BrainyQuote.com. Retrieved September 29, 2016, from BrainyQuote.com: https://www.brainyquote.com/quotes/quotes/a/aristotle143026.html

[8] Henry David Thoreau. (n.d.). BrainyQuote.com. Retrieved September 29, 2016, from BrainyQuote.com: https://www.brainyquote.com/quotes/quotes/h/henrydavid103440.html

[9] King, M. L., & Washington, J. M. (1986). A testament of hope: The essential writings of Martin Luther King, Jr. San Francisco, CA: Harper & Row.

[10] Shakespeare, W., & Hosley, R. (1954). The tragedy of Romeo and Juliet. New Haven, CT: Yale University Press.

[11] Lennon, J. (n.d.). John Lennon Quotes. Retrieved September 29, 2016, from http://www.goodreads.com/author/quotes/19968.John_ Lennon

Wedshock

There's more to marriage than happily ever after.

Let's just be honest. One day you're a wild and free bachelor/bachelorette, and the next you're committing to a lifelong roommate...that you share your dreams, money, emotions, and even your toothpaste with. That's nothing short of a gigantic adjustment, and yet, the resources available to help you navigate your newlywed life are microscopic compared to the businesses, publications and experts available to help you plan a wedding, buy a dress, or organize a rehearsal dinner.

Not cool.

That's why we created Wedshock: to support newlyweds in a fun, honest and helpful way while they're experiencing the highs and lows of new marriage. No need to navigate this unpredictable season alone. We've got you.

For Bride-to-be and Newlywed Resources, visit wedshock.com.

> Facebook.com/wedshock
> Instagram @wedshock
> Twitter @wedshock

Made in the USA
Monee, IL
16 January 2020